ANORAK OF LOVE

ROCK'N'ROLL MINDGAMES

mike bennett vs frank holli

First edition published 2004 by Complete Publications,
c/o 83 Albemarle Road, South Bank, York YO23 1EP
www.anorakoflove.com

Cover Design by Stone Soup, Fishergate Centre,
York YO10 4FB
www.stone-soup.co.uk

ISBN 0-9525823-1-7

Printed and bound by Peter Turpin Associates
www.pturpin-associates.co.uk

Special Thanks to: Ashok Kallumpram, Janet Hewison,
Michelle Fletcher, Peter Byrne, Tom Sharp & all at Stone
Soup, Simon Buckle at Peter Turpin's, Dave Martin, Keith
Ashton and all we have bored.

 Are you guilty of the **arrogant** tendency to judge people solely on their record collections?

 If involved in a relationship, do you subtly attempt to **weed out** the more dubious areas of your partner's musical tastes, gradually replacing them with your own?

 Do you feel that certain oafish cover versions merit a minimum 5-year **custodial sentence**?

 When expecting guests, have you ever endeavoured to have a **specific track** playing when a particular person enters the house?

 IF ANY OF THE ABOVE SAYS ANYTHING TO YOU ABOUT *YOUR* LIFE, **WELCOME TO ANORAK OF LOVE.**

Anorak Of Love is <u>not</u> a quiz book, a trivia book or simply a game. It invites rock'n'roll obsessives into a seriously addictive world.

Each page challenges self-confessed Anoraks to match, or even better, a specific – sometimes surprising – target. Anorak Of Love can be enjoyed in private, or in public with close friends or rivals.

Its contents will spin round in your head like the worst record you ever bought. It is a book you will become desperate to put down.

This edition of **Anorak Of Love** concentrates solely on **UK TOP 75 HIT SINGLES**. Album tracks, B-sides, your brother's ex-girlfriend's cousin's DIY lost classic 7" are **all invalid**.

⬤ If you are answering a challenge with the title of a hit, you must also **name the artist.**

⬤ Most answers pertain to the actual **title** of a hit, or its *specific* contents.

⬤ The suggested Anorak targets **do not include** the offered example(s).

⬤ An Anorak response to a target is valid when there exists **more than one version of a song**, providing the artists are named.

● Certain records are valid answers to **more than one category**.

● The suggested **Anorak Targets** for each category have been fanatically researched by the authors.

● The authors accept that a degree of controversy may surround certain categories, especially those with a subjective element. They also accept that, despite their preparation, they may well be out-Anoraked by some readers. If so, please contact us.

● You may wish to assemble fellow Anoraks in a smoke-filled room and, heavily armed, place bets on your performances. You may even wish to appoint a referee. Come and have a go, if you think you're sad enough…

DIRECTOR'S CUTS

A number of categories, sadly, failed to make the final 140, often because they were too subjective, or proved impractical to research. The authors have nonetheless included them, and invite input from connoisseur Anoraks.

(viii)

THE
AUTHORS

Mike Bennett

FIRST RECORD EVER BOUGHT

Let It Be – Beatles (No.2 1970)

"Complete with a (then rare) picture sleeve, later sold at a time of extreme 1980s poverty for £6…"

MOST EMBARRASSING PURCHASES

AGED 10-15 Chirpy Chirpy Cheep Cheep – Middle Of The Road (No.1, 1971)

"It seemed lyrically ground-breaking at the time…"

AGED 15-20 Nobody Does It Better – Carly Simon (No.7, 1977)

"I imagined a girl, sitting at the foot of a bed, singing an a cappella version to me, and me only…"

AGED 20-25 Sultans Of Swing – Dire Straits (No.8, 1979)

"There seemed no suggestion of future atrocities…"

AGED 25-30 The Power Of Love – Jennifer Rush (No.1, 1985)

"The unique fusion of operatic vocals and a mini-skirt was mesmerising…"

AGED 30 and above Believe – Cher (No.1, 1998)

"By its sixth week at no.1, I capitulated to a vocoder and an older woman…"

(x)

Frank Holli

FIRST RECORD EVER BOUGHT

Little Willy – Sweet (n.4 1972)

"Singing it in school changing rooms became banned, forcing me to grab it with both hands…"

MOST EMBARRASSING PURCHASES

AGED 10-15 Nice One Cyril – Cockerel Chorus (No.14, 1973)

"A universal anthem of brotherhood, I had no idea it was about football…"

AGED 15-20 The Logical Song – Supertramp (No.7 1979)

"Now attempting to be intellectual, I mistakenly chose a Pop Prog atrocity, and duly asked for it in Woolworth's in a helium voice…"

AGED 20-25 Hey You (The Rocksteady Crew) – Rocksteady Crew (No.6, 1983)

"It inspired me to misguidedly wear leg-warmers for a single, ill-fated day"

AGED 25-30 Bring Your Daughter …To The Slaughter – Iron Maiden (No.1 1991)

"It inspired me to misguidedly wear a headband for a single, ill-fated day"

AGED 30 and above Re-Rewind The Crowd Say Bo Selecta – Artful Dodger feat. Craig David (No.2, 1999)

"I believed Pop had discovered a vital new talent, ignoring the dire warning inherent in a cartoon beard"

(xii)

WE GO OUT ANY NIGHT WE WANT

Hit songs about days of the week (other than Saturday)

(e.g. *Blue Monday* – New Order, no.9 1983, *She Left Me On Friday* – Shed Seven, no.11 1998)
[NOTE: Day must be in title]

Anorak Targets
Monday 12   Tuesday 6
Wednesday 1   Thursday 1
Friday 15   Sunday 25

WHAT'S ANOTHER YEAR?

Hit songs about months of the year

(e.g. *January* – Pilot, no.1 1975, *The Funeral {September 25th 1977}* – Thuli Dumakude, no.75 1988)

[NOTE: Month must be in title, 'march' as verb or noun **invalid**, 'may' used not in reference to the month, e.g. 'Maggie May' – Rod Stewart, no.1 1971, **invalid**]

Anorak Targets				
January 3	February 2	March 1	April 4	May 2
June 2	July 2	August 1	September 6	October 1
November 3	December 5			

LONG SHOT KICK DE BUCKET

Hit songs involving a single human fatality (other than suicide [see 4], executions [see 7] and murders by women [see 8])

(e.g. *Tell Laura I Love Her* – Ricky Valance, no.1 1960, *The Day That Curly Billy Shot Down Crazy Sam McGee* – Hollies, no.24 1973)

Anorak
Target
25

IT'S ALL ME! ME! ME!

Hit songs involving a suicide

(e.g. *Emma* – Hot Chocolate, no.3 1974)
[NOTE: Songs referring to suicide *in general* e.g. 'Theme
From M.A.S.H. (Suicide is Painless)' – Mash, no.1
1992, **invalid**]

Anorak
Target
6

YOU ONLY LIVE TWICE

Hit songs involving two fatalities
(e.g. *I Shot The Sheriff* – Eric Clapton,
no.9 1974)
[The song states that the narrator "did not kill the deputy",
hence the deputy presumably also expired. NOTE: 'Stan' –
Eminem, no.1 2000, technically involves **3** fatalities, as the
crazed fan's girlfriend {in the boot of his car} was pregnant]

Anorak
Target
7

BODY COUNT

Hit songs involving more than twenty fatalities

(e.g. *English Civil War* – The Clash,
no.25 1979)
[NOTE: Plane crashes {**3/4 hits**} valid. Battles and World
War One and Two activities **invalid** {see 39 & 40}]

**Anorak
Target
8**

'TIS A FAR, FAR, BETTER THING...

Hit songs referring to an execution

(e.g. *Gary Gilmore's Eyes* – Adverts,
no.18 1977)
[NOTE: Gilmore was convicted of two murders, and chose to
face a firing squad. Thus the record, along with Eminem's
'Stan', is one of the only hits to deal with exactly
three fatalities]

**Anorak
Target
6**

DEADLIER THAN THE MALE

Hit songs involving murder(s) by a woman

(e.g. *Frankie And Johnny* – Sam Cooke, no.30 1963)

[NOTES: Hits where it is unclear whether a woman actually *personally* committed murder e.g. 'Ma Baker' – Boney M, no.2 1977, **invalid**]. Perhaps the most famous song of the genre, the much-recorded '**Miss Otis Regrets**' {written by Cole Porter c.1930} failed to chart for anybody. An excellent version by the Lemonheads exists as a bonus track on their 1993 album 'Come On Feel The Lemonheads']

Anorak
Target
6

GRAVEYARD SMASH

Hits inappropriate at a funeral
(excluding cremations)

(e.g. *Going Underground* – The Jam,
no.1 1980)

[NOTE: Cremations **invalid** owing to the large number of hits
with the word "fire" in their title. 'Fire' – The Crazy World Of
Arthur Brown, no.1 1968, would surely have been the best
crematorium selection…]

Anorak
Target
10

THE MIGHTY ZIM

Hits with Bob Dylan songs

(e.g. *If Not For You* – Olivia Newton-John, no.7 1971, *I'll Be Your Baby Tonight* – Robert Palmer and UB40, no.6 1990)

Anorak
Target
30

AND WHY NOT...?

Hit songs which are the title of a film, yet have nothing to do with it

(e.g. *They Shoot Horses Don't They?* – Racing Cars, no.14 1977, *The Wicker Man* – Iron Maiden, no.9 2000, *Sunset Boulevard* – Michael Ball, no.72 1993)

**Anorak
Target
50 plus**

HIRSUITS YOU, SIR!

Solo No.1 hits from an artist sporting a beard

(e.g. *The Roussos Phenomenon (EP)* – Demis Roussos, no.1 1976)

[NOTE: Artists who *previously* wore a beard, or later grew one, **invalid**. The beard must have been sported at the time of the hit]

Anorak Target 19

THESPIAN TENDENCIES

Hit songs referring to specific actors/actresses (in the title)

(e.g. *John Wayne Is Big Leggy* – Haysi Fantayzee, no.11 1982, *Ballad Of Chasey Lain* – Bloodhound Gang, no.15 2000)
[NOTE: Actors/actresses from porn films **valid**]

Anorak Target 14

BIGGER THAN JESUS...

Hits with Beatles/Lennon-McCartney songs which *weren't* hits for the Beatles

(e.g. *When I'm Sixty Four* – Kenny Ball and his Jazzmen, no.43 1967, *Dear Prudence* – Siouxie and The Banshees, no.3 1983)

[NOTE: Hits written by a lone Beatle e.g. 'Come And Get It' – Badfinger, no.4 1970 {McCartney}, **invalid**]

> Anorak
> Target
> 31

FRIGGIN' IN THE RIGGIN'

Hit songs referring to specific (i.e. named) ships/nautical vessels

(e.g. *Kon-Tiki* – Shadows, no.1 1961)

Anorak
Target
10

THE DAY BEFORE YOU CAME

Hit songs alluding to the loss of virginity

(e.g. *I Recall A Gypsy Woman* – Don Williams, no.13 1976)

[NOTE: Williams was "held to the gypsy woman's bosom at the age of just seventeen", which would (presumably) count for most men…]

Anorak
Target
4

THREE'S A CROWD

Hit songs concerning involvement in a love triangle

(e.g. *Torn Between Two Lovers* – Mary MacGregor, no.4 1977)
[NOTE: Hits referring to merely cheating while in a supposedly committed relationship **invalid** {see 37}]

**Anorak
Target
12**

COLD FEET

Hit songs suggesting a determination to avoid future relationships altogether

(e.g. *I'll Never Fall in Love Again* – Bobbie Gentry, no.1 1969)
[NOTE: Hits suggesting a desire to be unattached in order to enjoy mindless rampant sexual activity e.g 'Single Life' – Cameo, no.15 1985, **invalid**]

**Anorak
Target
10**

Epic
18

NAVEL GAZING

Eponymous hits (i.e. song title identical to name of artist[s])

(e.g. *Mr. Blobby* – Mr. Blobby, no.1 1993)
Star Turn On 45 (Pints) -- Star Turn On
45 (Pints), no.45 1981)
[NOTE: Songs simply including the artist's name in the title,
e.g. 'Wham Rap' by Wham! **invalid**. Song titles where there
is only a minor variation e.g. 'Chairm<u>a</u>n Of The Board' –
Chairm<u>e</u>n Of The Board also **invalid**]

Anorak
Target
17

BASTARDS

Hit songs alluding to illegitimate offspring

(e.g. *Embarrassment* – Madness, no.4 1980)
[NOTE: See also DODGY DADS {Category 20}]

DODGY DADS

Hit songs about questionable fathers

(e.g. *Daddy Don't You Walk So Fast* – Daniel Boone, no.17 1971)

DODGY MUMS

Hit songs about questionable mothers

(e.g. *Ma Baker* – Boney M, no.2 1977)

Anorak
Target
3(?)

LET'S SPEND THE KNIGHT TOGETHER

Hits with Rolling Stones songs

(e.g. *Satisfaction* – Devo, no.41 1978, *Honky Tonk Women* – Pogues, no.56 1992)

ON THE GAME

Hit songs referring to prostitution

(e.g. *The House Of The Rising Sun* – Animals,
no.1 1964)
[NOTE: A cursory listen to this traditional song's lyrics
confirm its subject matter]

**Anorak
Target
11**

23

THEY SOLD THEIR SOULS FOR ROCK'N'ROLL

Hit songs alluding to a churchman (in the title)

(e.g. *Stripper Vicar* – Mansun, no.19 1996)

Anorak
Target
6

LET'S GO RIGHT BACK...

Hit songs alluding to the Old Testament
(excluding those with Angels, the Devil, Satan, Holy, Eden, Paradise & God in the title)

(e.g. *Samson and Delilah* – Middle of the Road, no.26 1972)

Anorak
Target
19

LET'S GO RIGHT BACK II

Hit songs alluding to the New Testament
(excluding those with Jesus, Angels, the Devil,
Satan, Holy, Jerusalem & God in the title)

(e.g. *I Am The Resurrection* – Stone Roses,
no.33 1992)
[NOTE: Hits employing the word 'resurrection' as a casual
metaphor e.g. 'Love Resurrection' – Alison Moyet, no.10
1984, **invalid**]

> **Anorak**
> **Target**
> **14**

SAY A LITTLE PRAYER

Hit songs referring to places of worship (in the title)

(e.g. *Winchester Cathedral* – New Vaudeville Band, no.4 1966, *Church Of The Holy Spook* – Shane MacGowan And The Popes, no.74 1994)
[NOTE: Non-specific or metaphorical ecclesiastical buildings **valid**]

Anorak
Target
18

MORE THAN A FELINE

Hit songs referring to cats (in the title)

(e.g. *Puss 'N' Boots* – Adam Ant, no.5 1983,
Walking My Cat Named Dog – Norma Tanega,
no.22 1966)

**Anorak
Target
21**

LOFT IN MUSIC

Hit songs with the word pigeon (in the title)

(e.g. *Spot The Pigeon* (EP) – Genesis, no.14 1977)

Anorak Target 3

SEVEN YEAR TWITCH

Hits referring to specific birds (other than pigeons) in the title

(e.g. *Disco Duck [Part One]* – Ricky Dees and his Cast of Idiots, no.6 1976)
[NOTE: References to 'Robin Hood' **invalid**]

Anorak Targets
Ducks 6   Bluebirds 6 Doves 6 Mockingbirds 5
Robins 5 Chickens 3 Cuckoos 3 Seagulls 2
Eagles 2 Turkeys 2 Roosters 2 Swans 2 Falcons 1
Geese 1 Hummingbirds 1 Nightingales 1 Sparrows 1
Owls 1 Flamingos 1 Peacocks 1 OTHERS 2

HOUNDS OF LOVE

Hit songs about specific (i.e. named) dogs

(e.g. *Roobarb and Custard* – Shaft, no.7 1991)
[NOTE: For the uninitiated, Roobarb is a dog, Custard a cat.
Songs about a dog whose name is not clearly specified e.g
'A Salty Dog' – Procul Harum, no.44 1969, **invalid**]

Anorak
Target
7

VOX POP

Hit songs which begin with a word or words sung a cappella

(e.g. *Hanging On The Telephone* – Blondie, no.5 1978, *Cum On Feel The Noize* – Slade, no.1 1973)

[NOTE: SCORING SYSTEM – One point for each <u>completed</u> word, regardless if repeated. {i.e. Hanging On The Telephone – "I'm in the phone-booth it's the…" – involves six completed words, Cum On Feel The Noize – "Baby baby baby.." involves three]

Anorak Objective
Seek Therapy

THE ARTIST LATTERLY KNOWN AS YUSUF ISLAM

Hits with Cat Stevens songs

(e.g. *First Cut Is The Deepest* – PP Arnold, no.18 1967 and Rod Stewart, no.1 1977)

Anorak
Target
5

32

ROCK IN A BARD PLACE

Hit songs which are the title of a Shakespeare play

(e.g. *Romeo and Juliet* – Dire Straits, no.8 1981)
[NOTE: Songs must be the *exact* title of a play]

Anorak
Target
3

ROCK OF PAGES

Hit songs whose title is also a work of English or American literature (excluding Shakespeare [see 32])

(e.g. *Wuthering Heights* – Kate Bush,
no.1 1978,
For Whom The Bell Tolls – Bee Gees,
no.4 1993)

[NOTE: Songs which simply *refer* to a literary work in their title e.g. 'Jungle Book Groove' – Jungle Book, no.14 1993, **invalid**]

Anorak
Target
18

WELL RESPECTED MAN

Hit versions of Ray Davies (Kinks) songs

(e.g. *Stop Your Sobbing* – Pretenders, no.34 1979)
[NOTE: The Kinks 1964 album track impressed the 14-year-old Ohio-based Chrissie Hynde, who made it the Pretenders' debut single fifteen years later. Between 1981 and 1984 she became Davies' common-law wife, giving birth to their daughter Natalie. Perhaps too ideally suited as a rock'n'roll couple, the relationship was inevitably turbulent. In 1984 Chrissie left Ray for bombast supremo Jim Kerr of Simple Minds]

**Anorak
Target
7**

GRIMLY FIENDISH

Hit records concerning characters from horror films

(e.g. *Norman Bates* – Landscape, no.40 1981)
[NOTE: References to the Addams Family **valid**, reference to general horror characters e.g. 'Monster Mash' – Bobby 'Boris' Pickett and the Crypt-Kickers, no.3 1973, **invalid**]

> **Anorak**
> **Target**
> **16**

JUST A WILD STAB

Hit songs about serial killers

(e.g. *Mack The Knife* – Bobby Darin, no.1 1959,
Mack The Knife – Louis Armstrong, no.24 1959,
Mack The Knife – Ella Fitzgerald, no.19 1960,
Mack The Knife – King Kurt, no.55 1984)

**Anorak
Target
6**

THE DARK END OF THE STREET

Songs alluding to cheating whilst supposedly in a stable, committed relationship

(e.g. *I Saw Mommy Kissing Santa Claus* – Beverley Sisters, no.6 1953)

[NOTE: The song generally believed to be the greatest cheating song in soul history, 'The Dark End Of The Street', was much recorded, but only made a mere no.77 in the US Billboard chart with James Carr's supreme 1967 version]

> Anorak
> Target
> 13

ORIGINAL GANGSTAS

Hit songs referring to specific named gangsters (in the title)

(e.g. *The Ballad of Bonnie and Clyde* – Georgie Fame, no.1 1967)

[NOTE: Only *verifiable real-life* gangsters **valid**. Fictitious gangsters or gangsters in general e.g. 'Gangsters' – The Specials, no.6 1979, **invalid**]

> Anorak
> Target
> 4

1914-1918

Hits referring to World War One

(e.g. *Snoopy vs The Red Baron* – Hotshots,
no.4 1973)
[NOTE: Hits must refer specifically to WWI only]

**Anorak
Target
5**

1939-1945

Hit records referring to World War Two

(e.g. *The Dambusters March* – The Central
Band of the Royal Air Force, conducted by AE
Sims OBE, no.18 1955)
[NOTE: Hits must refer specifically to WWII only]

**Anorak
Target
9**

THE GREY & THE BLUE

Hit songs about the American Civil War

(e.g. *The Night They Drove Old Dixie Down* –
Joan Baez, no.6 1971)
[NOTE: 'Billy Don't Be A Hero' – Paper Lace, no.1 1974 is
believed to be set in the American Civil War, though its lyrics
don't specify the conflict]

**Anorak
Target
?**

THIN WHITE DUKE

Hits with David Bowie songs

(e.g. *The Man Who Sold The World* – Lulu, no.3, 1974)

Anorak
Target
6

LOST IN TRANSLATION

Hit songs which were originally in a different language

(e.g. *Those Were The Days* – Mary Hopkin,
no.1 1968, originally in Russian)
[NOTE (A): This category does *not* refer to songs simply in a
language other than English. NOTE (B): 'Ave Maria'
{originally in Latin, a hit 3 times}, 'Que Sera' {partially in
Spanish, a hit 4 times} and 'Never On A Sunday' {originally
in Greek, a hit 5 times} **all invalid**. Two songs were written in
English but were UK hits in a different language, hence the
English target]

Anorak Targets:
French 7 Russian 1 German 1 Italian 2 English 2

GOBSMACKED!

Instrumental No.1 records

(e.g. *Eye Level* – Simon Park Orchestra,
no.1 1973)

Anorak
Target
13

COMPACT AND BIJOU

Hit songs referring to low-budget accommodation (excluding caravans)

(e.g. *Wigwam Bam* – Sweet, no.4 1972)
[NOTE: Metaphorical or unfeasible accommodation e.g.
'Living On The Ceiling' – Blancmange, no.7 1982, **invalid**]

**Anorak
Target
14**

DIAMOND GEEZER

Hits with Neil Diamond songs

(e.g. *The Boat That I Row* – Lulu, no.6 1967)
[NOTE: Despite an embarrassing air-punching housewives'
choice image, Diamond wrote, unbeknown to many, his fair
share of classic songs. He penned the title track for Johnny
Cash's 2000 'Solitary Man' album.]

Anorak
Target
9

COULD IT BE FOREVER...?

Hit songs with an endless refrain

(e.g. *Hey Jude* – Beatles, no.1 1968)
[NOTE: Once Bob Dylan had shattered the 3-minute barrier
with 'Like A Rolling Stone', no.4 1965 {5 mins 59 secs}, the
occasional risk was taken]

Anorak
Target
5

JUST PUT YOUR LIPS TOGETHER AND BLOW

Hit songs involving whistling

(e.g. *I Was Kaiser Bill's Batman* – Whistling Jack Smith, no.5 1967, *Jennifer Eccles* – Hollies, no.7 1968)
[NOTE: Roger Whittaker hits {7} **invalid**]

**Anorak
Target
16**

THEY THINK IT'S ALL OVER

Hit songs with a false ending

(e.g. *Hello Goodbye* – Beatles, no.1 1967)
[NOTE: Hit songs which stop in the middle for no apparent reason e.g. 'Blue Monday' – New Order, no.9 1983 and no.3 1988, **invalid**]

**Anorak
Target
3**

WHAT DID THEY EVER DO FOR *US?*

Hit songs/records in Latin

(e.g. *Veni Vidi Vici* – Ronnie Hilton, no.12 1954)
[NOTE: Songs/records when merely title is in Latin **valid**]

**Anorak
Target
17**

MORGUE THAN A FEELING

Posthumous <u>solo</u> no.1 hits

(e.g. *Living On My Own* – Freddie Mercury,
no.1 1993)
[NOTE: 'Solo' equals credited to one named artist only]

**Anorak
Target
10**

QUE?

Hit songs with largely incomprehensible titles

(e.g. *Dick-a-Dum-Dum (King's Road)* – Des O'Connor, no.14 1969, *Ooh-Wakka-Do-Wakka-Day* – Gilbert O'Sullivan, no.8 1972, *Goo Goo Barabajagal (Love Is Hot)* – Donovan, no.12 1969)

**Anorak
Target
50-plus**

DUCK-WALK THIS WAY

Hits with Chuck Berry songs

(e.g. *Memphis Tennessee* – Dave Berry,
no.19 1963)
[NOTE: Despite the embarrassment of 'My Ding-a-Ling', no.1
1972, Chuck remains perhaps one of the greatest vernacular
poets of his generation]

**Anorak
Target
12**

52

The
Silver Spotlight
Series

I'D RATHER GO BLIND

Hit songs referring to masturbation

(e.g. *The Winker's Song* – Ivor Biggun, no.22
1978, *I Touch Myself* – Divinyls, no.10 1991)

Anorak
Target
10

JUST SAY NO!

Hit songs clearly condemning the use of drugs…

(e.g. *Just Say No* – Grange Hill Cast, no.5 1986)

Anorak Target 9

JUST SAY YES!

Hit songs indicating that illegal substances have been involved, and suggesting a much more liberal attitude…

(e.g. *Caned And Unable* – Hi-Gate, no.12 2000,
We Call It Acieed – D Mob, no.3 1988,
Golden Brown – Stranglers, no.2 1982)
[NOTE: Hits clearly written under the influence of hallucinogenic drugs e.g. 'I Can Hear The Grass Grow' – Move, no.5 1967, though not directly referring to them, **invalid**]

**Anorak
Target
22**

YOU MUST REMEMBER THIS...

Hit songs alluding to historical incidents (excluding World War One and Two related events [see 39 & 40])

(e.g. *St. Valentine's Day Massacre (EP)* – Motorhead & Girlschool, no.5 1981)
[NOTE: For death completists, the massacre involved seven fatalities, including one innocent bystander]

Anorak Target 9

LOOK AT THAT CAVEMAN GO...

Hit songs inspired by prehistory

(e.g. *Brontosaurus* – The Move, no.7 1970)
[NOTE: Songs referring to the Flintstones **valid**, but
'Piltdown Rides Again' – The Piltdown Men, no.14 1961,
invalid. Piltdown Man turned out to be a 1953 hoax, despite
Viv Stanshall's (d. 1995) creditable narration on Mike
Oldfield's 1973 album 'Tubular Bells']

**Anorak
Target
12**

THE KING OF REGGAE

Hits with Bob Marley songs

(e.g. *No Woman No Cry* – Fugees, no.2 1996,
No Woman No Cry – Londonbeat, no.64 1991)

Anorak
Target
7

OI! GET YER 'AND OUT!

Hit songs by specific puppets

(e.g. *Reet Petite* – Pinky and Perky,
no.47 1993,
Boom Boom – Basil Brush feat. India Beau,
no.44 2003)
[NOTE: Animated characters e.g. The Smurfs and people in
suits e.g. Mr. Blobby, **invalid**]

**Anorak
Target
8**

SHUT UP AND DEAL

Hit songs about specific playing cards (in the title)

(e.g. *Jack O' Diamonds* – Lonnie Donegan, no.14 1957)

[NOTE: 'Deck Of Cards' – Max Bygraves, no.13 1973, **invalid**. References to non-specific cards e.g. 'From A Jack To A King' – Ned Miller, no.2 1963, also **invalid**]

Anorak
Target
6

GIRL, YOU'LL BE A WOMAN ULTIMATELY

Hit songs we were duped into thinking were about a woman, but turned out to be about a young girl

(e.g. *Save Your Kisses For Me* – Brotherhood Of Man, no.1 1976)

Anorak
Target
6

WHAT'S THIS ONE ABOUT...?

Hit songs where the title appears to have nothing to do with what they're singing about...

(e.g. *Alternate Title* – The Monkees, no.2 1967, *Cognoscenti vs Intelligentsia* – Cuban Boys, no.4 1999, *Hindu Times* – Oasis, no.1 2002)

Anorak Target 30-plus

SHEER TEUTONIC EFFICIENCY

Hits in German

(e.g. *Das Boot* – U96 no.18 1992,
Wunderbar – Ten Pole Tudor no.16 1981)
[NOTE: Hits where just title is in German **valid**]

| Anorak
Target
19 |

THE MATH

Hit records alluding to mathematics

(e.g. $E=MC^2$ – Big Audio Dynamite,
no.11 1986)

[NOTE: Hits which relate more to *physics* e.g. 'Einstein A
Go-Go' – Landscape, no.5 1981, and hits which are
mathematically incorrect e.g. '2+2=5' – Radiohead, no.15
2003, all **invalid**]

**Anorak
Target
11**

DROP THE HAMMER...

Hit songs alluding to tools (in the title)

(e.g. *Monkey Wrench* – Foo Fighters,
no.12 1997)

**Anorak
Target
11**

64

SHAFTED

Hit songs concerning mining

(e.g. *New York Mining Disaster 1941* – Bee Gees, no.12 1967, *Outdoor Miner* – Wire, no.51 1979)
[NOTE: 'The Theme From Shaft' – Isaac Hayes, no.4 1971, **invalid,** John Shaft being a cop, rather than a pit]

Anorak
Target
7

'RURAL', RATHER THAN URBAN

Hit songs alluding to agriculture (excluding cowboys, horses, fields and harvests)

(e.g. *Ol' Macdonald* – Frank Sinatra, no.11 1960, *Muck It Out!* – Farmers Boys, no.48 1983)

Anorak
Target
27

GETTING WOOD

Hit songs referring to a particular type of wood (in the title)

(e.g. *Theme From 'Mahogany'* – Diana Ross, no.5 1976)

TRANS-EUROPE EXPRESSION

No.1 hits which were Eurovision winners

(e.g. *Puppet On A String* – Sandie Shaw,
no.1 1967)

[NOTE: While 'Congratulations' – Cliff Richard *did* reach no.1
in the UK in 1968, it controversially only came second in the
contest. We were, as ever, robbed]

Anorak
Target
6

(?   )

No.1 hits involving parenthesis (brackets)

(e.g. *Ernie (The Fastest Milkman In The West)*
– Benny Hill, no.1 1971, *I'll Do Anything For
Love (But I Won't Do That)* – Meat Loaf,
no.1 1993)
[NOTE: The words (remix) or (EP) etc. **invalid**]

Anorak
Target
41

THE BITCH IS BACK

Hits with Elton John songs

(e.g. *Don't Let The Sun Go Down On Me* –
Oleta Adams, no.33 1999)
[NOTE: See Epilogue "**ANTICHRISTS**"]

Anorak
Target
3

TOFFS

Hit songs referring to lesser members of the aristocracy (i.e. not King, Queen, Prince or Princess)

(e.g. *Sultans Of Swing* – Dire Straits, no.8 1979)
[NOTE: Lords, Ladies and Knights **invalid**]

Anorak Target 9

ORCHESTRAL MANOEUVRES

Hit songs lifted from classical music

(e.g. *Minuetto Allegretto* – Wombles,
no.16 1974)
[The tune is from Mozart's 41st Symphony in C. Claim a
bonus point if able to name the piece of classical music]

**Anorak
Target
*multissimo***

caroline cooper

71

WONDER OF YOU

Hits with Stevie Wonder songs

(e.g. *Gangsta's Paradise* – Coolio, no.1 1995)
[The original is 'Pastime Paradise', on SW's 1976 album
'Songs In The Key Of Life']

**Anorak
Target
13**

72.

A-Z

Hits about specified thoroughfares
(in the title)

(e.g. *Electric Avenue* – Eddy Grant, no.2 1983, no.5 2001)

[NOTE: Targets divided into thoroughfares that **definitely** exist {e.g. Electric Avenue, Brixton UK}, and those whose existence is **questionable** {e.g. Devil Gate Drive – Suzi Quatro, no.1 1974}. While some song titles contain street names that probably exist in *most* UK cities, the song may well *not* be about that particular thoroughfare, and is hence 'questionable']

Anorak Targets
Definite 10   Questionable 17

THE DICK VAN DYKE EXPERIENCE

Hit songs about a specific area of London (excluding football songs)

(e.g. *Only Living Boy In New Cross* – Carter The Unstoppable Sex Machine, no.7 1992, *Hersham Boys* – Sham 69, no.6 1979)

Anorak
Target
23

A BIG COUNTRY

Hit songs alluding to American states (other than New York)

(e.g. *North To Alaska* – Johnny Horton, no.23 1961)

Anorak Targets
California 18 Texas 5 Tennessee 4 Alabama 4
Kansas 3 Georgia 3 Mississippi 2 Indiana 2 Ohio 2
Kentucky 2 Massachusetts 1 Washington 1
Hawaii 1 Missouri 1 Carolina 1 Dakota 1

UP THE REDS

Hit songs about a communist country

(e.g. *Cuba* – The Gibson Brothers, no. 12 1980)
[NOTE: Countries formerly communist **valid**. China as a ceramic **invalid**. Adjectives e.g. 'Cuban Pete' – Jim Carrey, no.31 1995, **invalid**]

Anorak
Target
13

METROPOLIS NOW

Hit songs about capital cities (excluding London and Paris)

(e.g. *One Night in Bangkok* – Murray Head, no.12 1984, *Drowning In Berlin* – Mobiles, no.9 1982, *Kingston Town* – UB40, no.4 1990)

Anorak Target 28

OUT OF TOWNERS

Hit songs referring to U.K. towns/cities other than London (in the title, excluding football songs)

(e.g. *Long Haired Lover From Liverpool* – Little Jimmy Osmond, no.1 1972, *Daytrip To Bangor* – Fiddler's Dram, no.3 1979, *Come To Milton Keynes* – Style Council, no.23 1985)

Anorak Target 24

WHOLE WIDE WORLD

Hit songs about countries

(e.g. *Boat To Bolivia* – Martin Stephenson &
The Daintees, no.70 1986)
[NOTE: Communist countries **invalid** – see 75. Hits which
do not *name* the country in their title e.g. 'Down Under' –
Men At Work, no.1 1983 **invalid**. Continents e.g. America or
Africa, **invalid**. Adjectives e.g. 'Spanish Stroll' – Mink
DeVille, no.20 1977, **invalid**. U.S.A. **valid**. Countries *within*
Africa **valid**]

Anorak Targets (by continent location):
South & Central America 18 Europe 10
Africa 7 Asia 6 North America & Canada 5
Oceania & Australasia 2

DROP THE PILOT

Hits about aviation

(e.g. *Drop The Pilot* – Joan Armatrading, no.11
1983, *Light Aircraft On Fire* – Auteurs,
no.58 1996)

Anorak
Target
26

LADY OF THE CANYON

Hits with Joni Mitchell songs

(e.g. *Big Yellow Taxi – Amy Grant*, no.20 1995)

Anorak
Target
6

GRATUITOUS SAX

Hit songs involving a totally gratuitous saxophone solo

(e.g. *Digging Your Scene* – Blow Monkeys, no.12 1986)
[All other Blow Monkeys hits {10} **invalid**]

**Anorak
Target
20 plus**

THE IMPOSTER

Hits with Elvis Costello songs

(e.g. *Alison* – Linda Ronstadt, no.66 1979)
[NOTE: Collaborations e.g. 'My Brave Face' – Paul
McCartney, no.18 1989, **invalid**]

Anorak
Target
3

IF THE CAP FITS

Hit songs referring to headgear
(in the title)

(e.g. *Homburg* – Procul Harum, no.6 1967)

WALKING MIRACLES

Hit songs referring to footwear (in the title)

(e.g. *Clog Dance* – Violinski, no.17 1979,
Michael And The Slipper Tree – Equals,
no.24 1969)
[NOTE: Perhaps the greatest footwear song, 'Shoes' by
Brook Benton {1931-88} released 1970, failed to make any
impression on the UK chart]

**Anorak
Target
24**

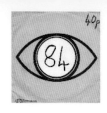

DO I LOOK COOL IN THIS?

Hit songs alluding to menswear in the title (excluding headgear and shoes)

(e.g. *Niall Quinn's Disco Pants* – A Love Supreme, no.59 1999, *Kool In A Kaftan* – B.A. Robertson, no.17 1980)

[NOTE: Unisex garments e.g. jeans or kaftans only valid if *clearly* specified which gender is wearing them]

Anorak
Target
28

DO I LOOK FAT IN THIS?

Hit songs referring to specific womenswear in the title (excluding headgear and shoes)

(e.g. *Leap Up And Down (Wave Your Knickers In The Air)* – St. Cecilia, no.12 1971, *Bikini Girls With Machine Guns* – Cramps, no.35 1990)

[NOTE: Unisex garments e.g. jeans or jackets only valid if *clearly* specified which gender is wearing them]

Anorak
Target
21

THE NAUGHTY BITS

Hit songs referring to buttocks, breasts or genitalia (in the title)

(e.g. *Cheeky Song (Touch My Bum)* – Cheeky Girls, no.2 2002, *Nipple To The Bottle* – Grace Jones, no.50 1982, *Erection (Take It To The Top)* – Cortina featuring BK & Madam Friction, no.48 2002) [NOTE: Double-entendres permitted. Use of the word 'bottom' when not referring to the buttocks, e.g. 'I Can't Tell The Bottom From The Top' – Hollies, no.7 1970, **invalid**]

Anorak Targets
Buttocks 16   Breasts 2   Genitals 15

THE MARY WHITEHOUSE EXPERIENCE

Hit records (excluding by Judge Dread) that received a BBC airplay ban

(e.g. *Bloodsport For All* – Carter The Unstoppable Sex Machine, no.48 1991, *Plastic Man* – The Kinks, no.31 1969)

[NOTE: *Temporary* bans e.g. for Tom Jones, following an overly "raunchy" rendition of 'It's Not Unusual' on 'Blue Peter' in 1965, **invalid.** Video bans **invalid**]

Anorak
Target
23

GETTING AWAY WITH IT

Hit songs which somehow avoided a BBC airplay ban

(e.g. *Walk On The Wild Side* – Lou Reed, no.10 1973)

Anorak
Target
7

THE ORIGINAL ORIGINALS

Hit songs which reached no.1 for more than one artist

[e.g. *Unchained Melody* – no.1 for Jimmy Young (1955), Righteous Brothers (1990), Robson & Jerome (1995) and Gareth Gates (2002)]

Anorak
Targets
Twice 15 Thrice 3

WHEN SMOKEY DOESN'T SING

Hits with Smokey Robinson songs

(e.g. *Tracks Of My Tears* - Linda Ronstadt,
no.42 1976,
Tracks Of My Tears – Go West, no.16 1993,
Tracks Of My Tears – Colin Blunstone,
no.60 1982)

**Anorak
Target
7**

BOOTY CALL

Hit songs referring to a one night stand

(e.g. *One Night Stand* – Let Loose, no.12 1995)

**Anorak
Target
a few…**

IT'S A MAN'S, MAN'S, MAN'S WORLD

Hit songs credited to a *solo* male, yet featuring an unidentified female vocalist

(e.g. *Lucky Stars* – Dean Friedman, no.3 1978)
[NOTE: 'Lucky Stars' features uncredited vocals by Denise Marsa.
Backing vocalists **invalid**, but samples **valid**. Female must be
named. Producers who frequently employ uncredited vocalists e.g.
Goldie {6 hits, largely featuring D. Charlermagne} **invalid**]

**Anorak
Target
18**

EXOTIC WOMEN?

Hit songs about girls of a specific nationality (in the title)

(e.g. *Liberian Girl* – Michael Jackson,
no.13 1989)

Anorak
Target
8

EXOTIC MEN?

Hit songs about men of a specific nationality (in the title)

(e.g. *I'm In Love With A German Film Star* – Passions, no.25 1981)

Anorak
Target
6

GENDER-BENDING

Hit songs which suggest a degree of sexual ambiguity (excluding Smiths/Morrissey songs)

(e.g. *Goodbye Sam, Hello Samantha* – Cliff Richard, no.6 1970)
[NOTE: Songs which are largely *unambiguous* e.g. 'Y.M.C.A.' – Village People, no.1 1978, **invalid**]

Anorak Target 8

YOU ARE WHAT YOU EAT (1)

Hit songs referring to fruits (in the title)

(e.g. *Blackberry Way* – Move, no.1 1968)

Anorak Targets
Apples 13 Bananas 11 Cherries 8
Strawberries 7 Peaches 5 Grapes 5
Oranges 4 Clementines 2 Raspberries/
Coconuts/Plums/Tangerines/
Lemons/Pineapples all 1 OTHERS 3

YOU ARE WHAT YOU EAT (2)

Hit songs referring to vegetables (in the title)

(e.g. *Charlie Big Potato* – Skunk Anansie, no.17 1999, *Gather In The Mushrooms* – Benny Hill, no.12 1961)

> **Anorak Target 10**

PRAWN SLIPPY

Hit songs referring to seafood (excluding fish)

(e.g. *Pulling Mussels (From The Shell)* – Squeeze, no.44 1980)
[NOTE: Whales, though eaten in some cultures, are mammals and thus **invalid**. Fish e.g. 'Help! I'm A Fish' – Little Trees, no.11 2001, **invalid**. Crustacea *only* are valid]

Anorak
Target
6

I'LL ASK THE WAITER...

Hit songs suggesting no vegetarian alternative (excluding poultry [see 29])

(e.g. *Black Pudding Bertha* – Goodies, no.19 1975)

Anorak
Target
9

CASH COWS

Hit songs referring to dairy products (in the title)

(e.g. *Say Cheese (Smile Please)* – Fast Food Rockers, no.10 2003)

REVVED UP

Hits with Al Green songs

(e.g. *Let's Stay Together* – Tina Turner, no.6 1983)

[NOTE: Green's constant Sex vs God dilemma resulted in him becoming a pastor of the Full Gospel Tabernacle in Memphis in 1976. The hits, on his new 'Myrrh' label, not unsurprisingly dried up]

Anorak Target 12

SACRED COWS

Hit records which are acclaimed classics, but are in fact terrible

(e.g. *Bohemian Rhapsody* – Queen, no.1 1975,
American Pie – Don McLean, no.2 1972,
Hotel California – Eagles, no.8 1977,
Angels – Robbie Williams, no.4 1997)

**Anorak
Target
Herd 'em up!**

101

ANSWER THE QUESTION!

Hit songs referring to our judicial system

(e.g. *Your Honour* – Pluto, no.19 1982)
[NOTE: Hits referring simply to a police *situation* **invalid**
– see 102]

Anorak
Target
14

ROZZERS

Hits alluding to definite police activity

(e.g. *Glam Rock Cops* – Carter The
Unstoppable Sex Machine, no.24 1994,
Caught By The Fuzz – Supergrass,
no.43, 1994)

**Anorak
Target
22**

YOU'VE BEEN FRAMED

Hit songs about miscarriages of justice

(e.g. *Hurricane* – Bob Dylan, no.43 1976)

Anorak
Target
3

SEE YOU IN COURT

Hit songs which prompted controversy over plagiarism

(e.g. *Sweet Little Mystery* – Wet Wet Wet, no.5 1987)

[NOTE: 'Sweet Little Mystery' effectively lifts wholesale from Van Morrison's 'Sense of Wonder', about which the legendary Irishman was less than amused. Meanwhile the startling similarity between Bob Marley's 'Buffalo Soldier' {no.4 1983} and the theme from the 'Banana Splits', later a hit for The Dickies {no.7 1979} went unnoticed]

> **Anorak Target 3**

HOMAGE FRAIS

Hit songs mentioning another recording artist (in the title)

(e.g. *Johnny Mathis' Feet* – American Music Club, no.58 1993, *Wood Beez (Pray Like Aretha Franklin)* – Scritti Politti, no.10 1984)

<table>
<tr><td>Anorak
Target
31</td></tr>
</table>

LOOKING UP TO THE BOSS

Hits with Bruce Springsteen songs

(e.g. *Blinded By The Light* – Manfred Mann's
Earth Band, no.6 1976)

Anorak
Target
5

IF YOU CAN USE SOME EXOTIC BOOZE...

Hit songs alluding to exotic drinks (including champagne)

(e.g. *Escape (The Pina Colada Song)* – Rupert Holmes, no.23 1980, *Pass The Courvoisier* – Busta Rhymes featuring P Diddy & Pharrell, no.16 2002)

> **Anorak Target 14**

108

MY SHOUT!

Hit songs about affordable alcoholic beverages

(e.g. *I Am A Cider Drinker* – Wurzels,
no.3 1976, *Two Pints Of Lager And A Packet
Of Crisps Please* – Splodgenessabounds,
no.7 1980)

**Anorak
Target
32**

WHAT'S WRONG WITH THIS PITCHER?

Hit songs referring to glass or ceramic receptacles

(e.g. *Melting Pot* – Blue Mink, no.3 1969,
Long Tall Glasses – Leo Sayer, no.4 1974)

THE SQUIGGLE

Hits with Prince songs

(e.g. *Nothing Compares 2U* – Sinead O'Connor,
no.1 Jan. 1990,
Nothing Compares 2U – MXM, no.68
June 1990)

Anorak Target 6

TAKING THE HISS

Hit songs referring to specific snakes

(e.g. *The Sidewinder Sleeps Tonight* – R.E.M, no.17 1993)

Anorak
Target
?

ALL IN THE GAME

Hit songs about a sport other than football/soccer (excluding running)

(e.g. *Chalk Dust - The Umpire Strikes Back* – Brat, no.19 1982, *Snooker Loopy* – Matchroom Mob with Chas and Dave, no.6 1986)

Anorak Targets
Boxing 8 Cycling 4 American Football 3
Cricket 2 Baseball 2 Bull Fighting 2
Pool/ Rugby/Hunting/Ice Hockey/
Skiing/Gymnastics/Figure Skating/ Table
Tennis ALL 1

EIGHTEEN WITH A MULLET

Hits by individual top-flight footballers (excluding team songs)

(e.g. *Fog On The Tyne (Revisited)* – Gazza and Lindisfarne, no.2 1990)
[NOTE: Hits by those with a *vague* footballing past e.g. Owen Paul {a Celtic junior, one hit 1986} and Rod Stewart {trials for Brentford F.C.} **invalid**]

Anorak
Target
5

DON'T YOU KNOW WHO I AM?

Hit songs about a famous person who is *not* name-checked (either forename or surname) in the title

(e.g. *Philadelphia Freedom* – Elton John, no.12 1975)
[NOTE: Sir Elton's curious song is actually about tennis star Billie Jean King, who gave him a tennis shirt]

Anorak Target 10

THE ONLY WHITE GUY WHO CAN SAY "LORD HAVE MERCY"

Hits with Van Morrison songs

(e.g. *Have I Told You Lately* – Rod Stewart, no.5 1993)

THE CHAT CREPT IN

Hit songs (excluding rap records) involving a section which is spoken (by the vocalist)

(e.g. *Honey Come Back* – Glen Campbell, no.4 1970, *Crying Over You* – Ken Boothe, no.11 1974)
[NOTE: Hits by Lou Reed/Velvet Underground and The Fall **invalid**]

Anorak Target 14

THE CHAT KEPT IN

Hit songs (excluding rap records) where the lead vocalist *only* talks

(e.g. *If* – Telly Savalas, no.1 1975)
[NOTE: Hits by Lou Reed/Velvet Underground and by
The Fall **invalid**]

**Anorak
Target
5**

CREASING UP

Hit songs incorporating laughter

(e.g. *Mad About You* – Bruce Ruffin, no.9 1972,
Where Do You Go To My Lovely – Peter
Sarstedt, no.1 1969)
[NOTE: Short laughs, chuckles, cackles or titters **valid**]

**Anorak
Target
15**

WHATEVER IT IS, LET'S DO IT (1)

Hit songs about a Hustle

(e.g. *British Hustle* – Hi Tension, no.8 1978)
[NOTE: 'Hustling' simply as a lifestyle choice e.g. 'You Gotta
Be A Hustler If You Wanna Get On' – Sue Wilkinson,
no.25 1980, **invalid**]

```
Anorak
Target
7
```

WHATEVER IT IS, LET'S DO IT (2)

Hit songs about a Shuffle

(e.g. *Seaside Shuffle* – Terry Dactyl and the Dinosaurs, no.2 1972)

Anorak Target 7

RAVE ON

Hits with Buddy Holly songs

(e.g. *Not Fade Away* – Rolling Stones,
no.3 1964)

**Anorak
Target
7**

ANORAKNOPHOBIA

Hit songs which you were determined not to like, but did

(e.g. *Back For Good* – Take That, no.1 1995, *Jump* – Van Halen, no.7 1984, *More Than A Feeling* – Boston, no.22 1977, *(Don't Fear) The Reaper* – Blue Oyster Cult, no.16 1978, *Sweet Child O' Mine* – Guns 'N' Roses, no. 6 1988)

**Anorak
Target
confess**

POP GOES THE EASEL

Hits inspired by painters or paintings

(e.g. *Matchstalk Men And Matchstalk Cats And Dogs* – Brian and Michael, no.1 1978)
[Inspired by the paintings of L.S.Lowry {1887-1976}]

Anorak
Target
4

CELLO HURRAY

Hits referring to classical composers (in the title)

(e.g. *Rock Me Amadeus* – Falco, no.1 1986)
[NOTE: Hits credited to orchestras **invalid**]

**Anorak
Target
9**

PUNCH THE CLOCK

Hit songs referring to a particular time (excluding midnight, midday or specific years) in the title

(e.g. *It's Four In The Morning* – Faron Young, no.3 1972, *3am* – Busted, no.1 2004)

```
Anorak
Target
15
```

ACID ROCK

Vitriolic hits

(e.g. *Positively 4th Street* – Bob Dylan,
no.8 1965)

Anorak
Target
12

BE HIS MIRROR

Hit versions of Lou Reed/Velvet Underground songs

(e.g. *Perfect Day* – Various, no.1 1997)

Anorak
Target
7

126

KEEPING UP

Hit songs involving the surname Jones (in the title)

(e.g. *Delilah Jones* – McGuire Sisters, no.24 1956)

VA VA VOOM

Hit songs involving traffic sound effects

(e.g. *Down In The Tube Station At Midnight* –
Jam, no.15 1978)
[NOTE: Trains, boats and planes **all valid**]

**Anorak
Target
14**

SO WHAT ARE YOU DRIVING?

Hit songs about specific cars

(e.g. *Heaven Is The Backseat Of My Cadillac* – Hot Chocolate, no.25 1976, *One Piece At A Time* – Johnny Cash, no.32 1976)

Anorak
Target
11

AIN'T FROM AROUND HERE, ARE YOU?

Hit songs about feelings of alienation

(e.g. *White Man (in Hammersmith Palais)* – Clash, no.32 1978)

Anorak
Target
7

130

FORMERLY 'TOM AND JERRY'

Hits with Simon & Garfunkel songs

(e.g. *Cecilia* – Suggs, no.4 1996)

Anorak
Target
9

A TRAVESTY OF A MOCKERY OF A SHAM

Classic songs that only made it to No.2

(e.g. *Ride A White Swan* – T.Rex, no.2 1970,
Common People – Pulp, no.2 1995)
[NOTE: An extra point for naming an abominable record
which kept it off the top. In the first instance 'Grandad' by
Clive Dunn, in the second 'Unchained Melody' by
Robson & Jerome]

> **Anorak
> Target
> 30 plus**

HELLO VIENNA!

Hits with rocked-up classical music

(e.g. *Sabre Dance* – Love Sculpture, no.5 1968)
[NOTE: Original by Russian composer **Khachaturian**
{1903-78}. Classical composer must be named]

Anorak
Target
12

NOT MUCH EQUIPMENT

A cappella hits

(e.g. *Don't Worry Be Happy* – Bobby McFerrin, no.2 1988)

Anorak
Target
8

SHAME, SHAME, SHAME

Dreadful novelty hits by credible artists

(e.g. *Hi Ho Silver Lining* – Jeff Beck, no.14
1967 & no.17 1972)

**Anorak
Target
7**

I'M RANDY, FLY ME...

Hits with songs written by
Randy Newman

(e.g. *I Think It's Going To Rain Today* – UB40, no.6 1980)

[NOTE: Newman contributed two songs {'I Don't Want To Hear It Anymore' and 'Just One Smile'} to Dusty Springfield's legendary 1968 album 'Dusty In Memphis'. The album criminally failed to chart]

Anorak
Target
6

A FAMILY AFFAIR

Father and daughter hit duets

(e.g. *Something Stupid* – Frank & Nancy Sinatra, no.1 1967)

REBELLIOUS JUKEBOX

Hits originally intended as B-sides

(e.g. *I Will Survive* – Gloria Gaynor,
no.1 1979)

[Originally intended as B-side of 'Substitute', which had
already reached no.2 for Clout the previous year. The rest is
karaoke history. NOTE: Intended A-side must be named]

**Anorak
Target
6**

BACK IN THE SADDLE

Hit songs alluding to equestrianism, *without* the word 'horse' in the title

(e.g. *Chestnut Mare* – Byrds, no.19 1971,
Mule Train – Frank Ifield, no.22 1963)

ANORAK'S FEAR OF THE POLLEN COUNT

Hit songs about specific flowers (other than roses)

(e.g. *Tulips From Amsterdam* – Max Bygraves, no.3 1958, *Sweet William* – Millie, no.30 1964, *Lilac Wine* – Elkie Brooks, no.16 1978)

Anorak
Target
32

LET'S HEAR IT FOR THE BOY

Hit songs whose titles are simply a boy's first name

(e.g. *Michael* – Highwaymen, no.1 1961, *Alfie* – Cilla Black, no.9 1966, *Sam* – Olivia Newton-John, no.6 1977)

[NOTE: Songs which merely *include* a boy's name e.g. 'Rikki Don't Lose That Number' – Steely Dan, no.58 1979, or repeat a boy's name e.g. 'Sven Sven Sven' – Bell and Spurling, no.7 2001, **invalid**]

**Anorak
Target
37**

MY MUM'S GOT THE ORIGINAL!

Hits with songs perhaps better known as being sung by Dusty Springfield

(e.g. *I Only Want To Be With You* – Bay City Rollers, no.4 1976)

Anorak
Target
8

CLIFF HANGING

Decent Cliff Richard records…?

(e.g. *Honky Tonk Angels* (withdrawn, 1975),
We Don't Talk Anymore – no.1 1979)
{NOTE: Cliff oafishly spurned credibility by (after much soul-searching) electing *not* to record Wreckless Eric's magnificent 1977 non-hit 'Whole Wide World'. He objected to the line "caressing her warm brown skin", which Wreckless stubbornly refused to change. Instead Cliff recorded Eric's 'Broken Doll' for his 1981 album 'Wired For Sound']

Anorak **Target** **Total Honesty**

EPILOGUE
(OF LOVE)

DIRECTOR'S SELECT

HANG THE DJ (1)
TOO GOOD FOR THE CHARTS

The following singles, perhaps for a combination of reasons, failed to make the UK Top 75 chart. The finger can only be pointed at lazy, egotistical, unadventurous DJs...

1) THE ADVENTURES OF GRANDMASTER FLASH ON THE WHEELS OF STEEL – Grandmaster Flash (1981)
2) THE SHIP SONG – Nick Cave (1990)
3) ALISON – Elvis Costello (1977)
4) NIGHT NURSE – Gregory Isaacs (1982)
5) WHOLE WIDE WORLD – Wreckless Eric (1977)
6) GIGANTIC – Pixies (1988)
7) PSYCHO KILLER – Talking Heads (1977)
 8) DAMAGED GOODS – Gang Of Four (1978)
9) TRANS-EUROPE EXPRESS – Kraftwerk (1977)
10) ANORAK SELECT
[NOTE: 'Brown Eyed Girl' – Van Morrison (1967, reissued 1971 and 1974) stubbornly failed to chart in the UK, though hit no.10 in the US in 1967. UK DJs are perhaps, for once, blameless, as in fairness they played it to death....]

HANG THE DJ (2)
ONLY JUST MADE IT...

The following singles *did* make it into the UK top 75, though to pitifully low positions. Again, a hard line must be taken against conservative, complacent, 'personality'-absorbed radio DJs...

1) **HERE COMES YOUR MAN** – Pixies (no.54, 1989)
2) **AFTERMATH** – Tricky (no. 69, 1994)
3) **INTO MY ARMS** – Nick Cave (no.53, 1997)
4) **RATTLESNAKES** – Lloyd Cole (no.65, 1984)
5) **I WISH HE DIDN'T TRUST ME SO MUCH** – Bobby Womack (no.64, 1985)
6) **LEAN PERIOD –** Orange Juice (no.74, 1984)
7) **EVERYBODY HERE WANTS YOU** – Jeff Buckley (no.43, 1998)
8) **HERE I COME** – Barrington Levy (no.41, 1985)
9) **THE SWEETEST GIRL** – Scritti Politti (no.64, 1981)
10) **ANORAK SELECT**

VOCALISTS (1)

Terrible voice, but great…

In our hideous wannabe/Pop Idol/Fame Academy/ reality-TV age, let's not forget to pay tribute to those who really <u>couldn't</u> sing, though quite magnificently…

1) SHANE MCGOWAN
2) KEVIN ROWLAND
3) JOHN LYDON
4) JOE STRUMMER
5) SHAUN RYDER
6) MARK E. SMITH
7) JONATHAN RICHMAN
8) LOU REED
9) BOB DYLAN
10) **ANORAK CHOICE**

VOCALISTS (2)

Great voice, but terrible…

And while we're at it, let us issue a warning against those who really <u>can</u> sing, yet, in many cases, substitute strangulated vocal gymnastics for genuine emotion…

1) CELINE DION
2) WHITNEY HOUSTON
3) ALISON MOYET
4) MARIAH CAREY
5) SEAL
6) R KELLY
7) ROLAND GIFT
8) SARAH BRIGHTMAN
9) PAVAROTTI
10) ANORAK VIEW

VOCALISTS (3)

Great, pure voices...

You can, perhaps, count them on the fingers of one hand. But let's try both...

1) SAM COOKE
2) KAREN CARPENTER
3) GREGORY ISAACS (no chart hits)
4) EMMYLOU HARRIS
5) TONY BENNETT
6) AARON NEVILLE
7) ARETHA FRANKLIN
8) JEFF BUCKLEY
9) AL GREEN
10) ANORAK CHOICE

I COULD HAVE DANCED LIKE A PRAT

10 hit records you *may* have danced like an absolute idiot to...(NOTE: Alcohol consumption is no excuse)

1) COME ON EILEEN – Dexy's Midnight Runners (no.1 1982)

2) PAPA'S GOT A BRAND NEW PIGBAG – Pigbag (no.3 1982)

3) I'M A BELIEVER – Monkees (no.1 1967)

4) HAPPY HOUR – Housemartins (no.3 1986)

5) FREE NELSON MANDELA – Special AKA (no.9 1984)

6) BLUE MONDAY – New Order (no.9 1983)

7) TIGER FEET – Mud (no.1 1974)

8) JUST CAN'T GET ENOUGH – Depeche Mode (no.8 1981)

9) THIS CHARMING MAN – Smiths (no.25 1983)

10) ANORAK CONFESSION

JUST STICK TO SINGING ABOUT GIRLS

10 most embarrassing political records

1) **RUSSIANS** – Sting (no.12 1985)
2) **ANOTHER DAY IN PARADISE** – Phil Collins (no.2 1989)
3) **BELFAST CHILD** – Simple Minds (no.1 1989)
4) **WE ARE THE WORLD** – USA For Africa (no.1 1985)
5) **SUN CITY** – Artists Against Apartheid (no.21 1985)
6) **NAZIS** – Roger Taylor (no.22 1994)
7) **THROUGH THE BARRICADES** – Spandau Ballet (no.6 1986)
8) **MUTUALLY ASSURED DESTRUCTION** – Gillan (no.32 1981)
9) **INVISIBLE SUN** – Police (no.2 1981)
10) **ANORAK CHOICE**

THERE'S MORE TO LIFE THAN GIRLS

10 decent political records

1) **SHIPBUILDING** – Robert Wyatt (no.35 1983)

2) **WE DON'T NEED THIS FASCIST GROOVE THING** – Heaven 17 (no.45 1981)

3) **BIKO** – Peter Gabriel, (no.38 1980)

4) **NELSON MANDELA** – Special AKA (no.9 1984)

5) **GHOST TOWN** – Specials (no.1 1981)

6) **(FOR GOD'S SAKE) GIVE MORE POWER TO THE PEOPLE** – Chi-Lites (no.32 1971)

7) **THE MESSAGE** – Grandmaster Flash (no.8 1982)

8) **ANARCHY IN THE UK** – Sex Pistols (no.33 1976)

9) **SIGN 'O' THE TIMES** – Prince (no.10 1987)

10) **ANORAK CHOICE**

TAMPERING WITH PERFECTION

10 songs which <u>shouldn't</u> have been covered...

1) **UNCHAINED MELODY -** Righteous Brothers, no.14 1965/no.1 1990 [Robson&Jerome, no.1 1995]

2) **IF YOU DON'T KNOW ME BY NOW** – Harold Melvin & The Bluenotes, no.9 1973 [Simply Red, no.2 1989]

3) **LIGHT MY FIRE** – Doors, no.7 1967
[Hits for Will Young (2002), UB40 (2000), Mike Flowers Pops (1996), Amii Stewart (1979), Jose Feliciano (1968)]

4) **I GOT YOU BABE** – Sonny & Cher, no.1 1965
[UB40 & Chrissie Hynde, no.1 1985]

5) **CRY ME A RIVER** – Julie London, no.22 1957 [Mari Wilson, no.27 1983, Denise Welch, no.23 1995]

6) **PRIVATE NUMBER** – Judy Clay & William Bell, no.8 1968 [911, no.3 1999]

7) **KNOCKIN' ON HEAVEN'S DOOR** – Bob Dylan, no.14 1973 [Guns 'N' Roses, no.2 1992, Eric Clapton, no.38 1975]

8) **ALISON** – Elvis Costello (did not chart 1976)
[Linda Ronstadt, no.66 1979]

9) **DIDN'T I (BLOW YOUR MIND THIS TIME)** – Delfonics, no.22 1971 [New Kids On The Block, no.8 1990]

10) **ANORAK DECLARATION**

MAD...

Ten artists who, despite hit singles of some merit, may well be completely bonkers, and possibly unemployable outside the Top 20...

1) BJORK
2) TORI AMOS
3) PRINCE
4) MICHAEL JACKSON
5) KEVIN ROWLAND
6) KATE BUSH
7) OL' DIRTY BASTARD (Wu Tang Clan)
8) SCOTT WALKER
9) JULIAN COPE
10) ANORAK ANALYSIS

ANTICHRISTS

"I am an antichrist…" snarled John Lydon at punk's year zero (1976). In reality, nowadays Mr Rotten appears as little more than an eccentric, curiously camp pantomime grandee. The same, however, cannot be said for the following…

1) PHIL COLLINS
Countless atrocities ('You Can't Hurry Love'), but to actually have to *deny* that you dumped your wife by fax…

2) STING
Despite a string of near-classic Police singles, we must not forgive that fake Jamaican accent, those innumerable jazzers, that 'slow' version of 'Roxanne' to make it 'moving'…

3) MICK HUCKNALL
The inability to do anything other than 'show off' a mediocre non-'soul' voice, that narcissistic version of 'Night Nurse'…

4) CLIFF RICHARD
Singing 'Congratulations' at Wimbledon, that Messiah-like 'Forgive Us Our Trespasses' pose during 'Millennium Prayer' in front of Holocaust footage…

ANTICHRISTS (CONT.)

5) ELTON JOHN

Ultimate parody of a pop star and, of course, *that* version of 'Candle In The Wind' in Westminster Abbey…

6) MARK KNOPFLER (Dire Straits)

Music at its most awesomely self-congratulatory, the absurd award of an MBE, inanities about microwave ovens…

7) ROBBIE WILLIAMS

The unbearable smugness of being, the ludicrous earnings, that smirk while singing 'Something Stupid'…

8) GEORGE MICHAEL

Deciding to make all future releases 'online only' in order to 'give something back', the belief that he's writing better songs than those 'half his age'…

9) CELINE DION

Relentless manipulative over-singing, as a poor substitute for real emotion. And, of course 'My Heart Must Go On'…(must it?)

10) ANORAK ADDITION

FURTHER READING

This Is Uncool (The 500 Greatest Singles Since Punk And Disco) – Garry Mulholland
The Heart Of Rock & Soul (The 1001 Greatest Singles Ever Made) – Dave Marsh
The Guinness Book Of Hit Singles – Ed. David Roberts
The Rough Guide To Cult Pop – Ed. Paul Simpson
The Great Rock Discography – Martin C. Strong
The Rough Guide To Rock – Ed. Peter Buckley
The NME Rock'n'Roll Years – Ed. John Tobler
31 Songs – Nick Hornby
Encylopedia Of Singles – Ed Paul Du Noyer
Lives Of The Great Songs – Ed. Tim De Lisle

info@anorakoflove.com